ORIGINAL STRENGTH FOR THE TACTICAL ATHLETE

ORIGINAL STRENGTH FOR THE TACTICAL ATHLETE

Chad Faulkner and Tim Anderson

OS PRESS

Original Strength for the Tactical Athlete by Chad Faulkner & Tim Anderson

Copyright © 2017 by Original Strength Systems, LLC. All rights reserved.

Cover design by Danielle "Dani" Almeyda.

Publishing Architect™, Sherrie Wilkolaski. www.publishingarchitect.com

Paperback
ISBN-10: 1-941065-34-1, ISBN-13: 978-1-941065-34-1
eBook
ISBN-10: 1-941065-35-X, ISBN-13: 978-1-941065-35-8

Library of Congress Number available upon request.

Contents

Acknowledgements

Thanks goes to God first, of course. He's offered me plenty of challenges but also has blessed me in so many ways. Without Him, this wouldn't be possible.

Thanks to my wife for taking the pictures inside the book and holding things down while I dream and work on my many goals as I look toward retirement. Thanks also goes to Dani Almeyda for editing the pictures.

Thanks to my two girls who have had a little time taken away from them as I've worked on this project.

Thanks to my parents who have been nothing less than the best as I've gone through the last 19 years of service. They've been there every step of the way through the trials and challenges. I can't forget that my mom and dad endured training and deployments without knowing where I was or what I was doing, long before the social media age made it easier to keep up.

Thanks to Tim for being my mentor and partner in this book.

Thanks to John Brookfield for facilitating my meeting Tim so many years ago and teaching me so much as well.

Thanks to all of my many mentors throughout my career in the military. There are too many to list.

Thanks to Richard King Photography for being a great friend and taking an awesome cover photo.

Thanks to John Usedom for his mentorship and guidance in this project.

Part of what drives me is having lost so many brothers-in-arms over the years... those who will never have the chance to be with their families again, continue to serve their country, set goals and reach them, grow old, or do things like write a book. I owe it to them to live a good life and complete the mission.

Introduction

I've always told people that I wish my body had an odometer. With all the miles I've both walked and run, I would like to know my current mileage so that I can get regular tune-ups. Having been in the U.S. Army for 19 years at the writing of this book, my body has been abused for years.

I spent seven and a half years as an Airborne Infantryman in the 82nd Airborne Division. This meant physical training every morning at 0630 (that's 6:30 a.m. in civilian time) at the latest, usually running. We typically ran four days a week and foot marched one day a week. A typical run averaged around four miles. A short day was at least two miles, and sometimes, we would do up to six. Foot marches that were done for physical training were typically four to six miles as well. If we were coming in early and doing something longer, it was usually eight to twelve miles with the occasional twenty-five miler. We would spend days to weeks in the field, carrying heavy loads, sleeping on the ground, usually getting little sleep, and not eating quite as much as we should. The life of an infantryman is not an easy one.

On top of all of this, we would jump out of airplanes carrying two-thirds of our bodyweight or more and hit the ground at a high rate of speed. Part of the agony of jumping is wearing the parachute harness and gear for hours leading up to the jump. As of this writing, I'm approaching 100 jumps.

Following my time in the Infantry, I moved over to Civil Affairs. While Civil Affairs, in general, isn't as hard on the body as being an infantryman, it is still considered a Special Operations career field. This means the highest of standards are expected. During my time in Civil Affairs, I was able to take a step back from running as much, but there were still plenty of physical demands and jumps out of airplanes.

There's also the matter of several deployments where I slept on cots for months at a time and carried a load around that probably averaged 75 pounds. My first Afghanistan trip was where I did the most walking of any deployment. We carried body armor, a full load of ammo, grenades, helmet, weapon, and assault pack. Most of the time, this equipment was carried on uneven, unforgiving terrain.

On my second trip to Afghanistan, 90 percent of what we did over the eight-month period was at night. If you've ever worn night-vision goggles, you know that depth perception isn't that great. So, you sometimes hit "phantom holes" or step off small ledges and get a good spinal compression as you stomp down carrying all that gear. In 2009, I had frequent lower-back pain setting in. Once when getting checked out, I had a Navy doctor give me the example that

when strapping on all that gear, it's like becoming obese overnight by adding all the weight to our joints without our bodies having time to adjust.

So, why the "tactical athlete" label on this book? Because many of the same rigors we put our bodies through as soldiers can also apply to others out there in the "tactical" realm of everyday life.

Soldiers are athletes in everything we do, from the physical training to basic soldier skills. We must be able to carry a fallen comrade out of a fight and be able to maneuver under the stress of being shot at while carrying a load. All of these things mean we require the physical skills of an athlete.

In April of 2009, I was working out at a local gym that was affiliated with a certain recent fitness trend. Doing some of these workouts involved kettlebells. At the time, I was doing what I now know are called "snatches," and I was absolutely destroying my forearms with poor technique. When trying to learn from the "coach" how to do it right, I got nothing.

Later, I had the opportunity coming up to earn a "Battling Ropes" certification through John Brookefield, who encouraged me to come out because everyone else attending was a kettlebell instructor. There, I met Tim Anderson, and the rest is history. I've stayed in touch with Tim ever since that day through deployments as well as in daily life. He has helped me to grow along the way, both physically and spiritually. I've taken this ride with him that led from some good ideas to "Becoming Bulletproof" to what we now know as "Original Strength." It's been a privilege and a blessing. Original Strength and the RESETs have paid dividends in helping me regain and maintain movement even after all the beating my body has taken.

In this book, I hope to bring some of this goodness to you and apply it to the tactical athlete. I have always been in shape, and having a squad that was "fit to fight" was something I prided myself in. But I wish I could turn back time and use Original Strength to make myself and my men that much better. My hope is that some of my warrior brethren will have the tools *Original Strength* provides to help them keep their ability to move and be strong for as long as they may live.

> We few, we happy few, we band of brothers;
>> For he to-day that sheds his blood with me
>> Shall be my brother...
>> —William Shakespeare

1

What Is a Tactical Athlete?

"Tactical athlete" is a term that's been thrown around lately, but what does it mean? Let's start by looking at the meaning of the two words as defined in *Merriam-Webster's Dictionary*:

Tactical: of, relating to, or used for a specific plan that is created to achieve a particular goal in war, politics, etc.

Athlete: a person who is trained in or good at sports, games, or exercises that require physical skill and strength

If you put these two together, you might say a *tactical athlete* is someone who is trained in exercises that require skill and strength to achieve a particular goal. That's not a bad definition, but I think it could be better and more specific. So here's my definition:

Tactical athlete: a person who trains for physical and mental skill, stamina, and strength in order to handle complex situations in non-permissive and stressful environments

I believe this definition sums up what a *tactical athlete* is and covers more than just members of the military. If you'll notice, I included the word *mental*. I've always believed the mental challenge is something that needs to be part of anyone's physical training program. More on mental skills later, but mental strength and stamina are developed through tough and challenging physical training.

During my days in the 82nd Airborne Division, we would stretch and run anywhere from three to five miles, usually up Ardennes Street and back. I always found it fascinating when we would be on our way back and pass the barracks where we started our run. Immediately, you would start seeing soldiers beginning to struggle or even fall back at times. The exhaustion of having passed by what they had mentally prepared for to be the end was difficult to overcome. This was one example of how we were being trained mentally. In combat, will you know where the end is? Most likely not.

I used to tell people that even Arnold Schwarzenegger couldn't pass our standard of a 12-mile foot march in three hours or less if he wasn't mentally prepared. My point being that you could have all the muscles and strength in the world, but if you weren't mentally prepared to carry your kit and load for that distance, you wouldn't make it. (I realize Arnold could pass our ruck standard. I just used his prowess to make a point.)

Let's look at some fitness areas that fall into the realm of the tactical athlete:

- **Strength:** Tactical athletes need to be able to generate strength and power in order to take down bad guys hand to hand, lift and move heavy equipment, get obstacles out of the way, or worst case, carry a wounded buddy or victim.

- **Grip strength:** If you don't have the grip strength to hold onto heavy objects, all the upper body strength in the world isn't going to help you. I recommend people do exercises that focus on grip strength. I'll talk about some specific grip strength exercises later in the book.

- **Endurance:** You must be able to endure not only long movements on foot but also long days of constant work. We've all had missions that were supposed to last "36 to 48 hours" and took much longer, sometimes weeks longer. So endurance doesn't just apply to long runs and foot movements. Also, consider the terrain you work on when thinking about your endurance. Do you have to worry about high elevation with thinner air? Are you or will you be working in areas of steep terrain?

- **Speed:** You may need to cover ground quickly or just move quickly in general. If you've ever been in a firefight and have had to maneuver for cover, you know that speed is critical to have on your side. Being shot at tends to increase your speed, but don't rely on that.

- **Skill:** There may be specific things you need to be strong at in your profession as a tactical athlete. Maybe you're on a prison extraction team, and your job is to take down an unruly prisoner. That could mean training to slam things to the ground… gently, of course. You may be a machine gunner in an infantry weapons squad and need to work your upper body more to carry the gun on long patrols and put it into action.

- **Mobility and stability:** This is mainly where Original Strength comes in. As tactical athletes, you may have a set of tasks you need to be ready and trained for. We all know that a plan rarely survives first contact with the enemy, so you must be prepared for anything. If you've done adequate training in the other areas and kept good stability and mobility, you'll be ready for anything physically.

This is just a snapshot of what a tactical athlete needs to be trained in. There are many more sub-tasks and even more when you get into specific jobs. One thing most of us know is that our jobs are dangerous and that anyone can "go down" at any time. This means the next man or woman has to be ready to step up. Long story short, you have to be prepared for anything. I can't stress this enough.

The tactical athlete must train regularly and with focus. There is no second place for us.

Stress

Stress plays a huge role in the professions of the tactical athlete and can be debilitating to performing the job. The better your level of fitness and training in your particular skill, the better you'll be able to combat the effects of stress.

Having been an instructor at the Special Warfare Center for such a long time, I've been able to observe the effects of stress first hand and then question students immediately after to find out how they felt. I've seen students not hear conversations they should have heard when they took place within three feet of them. I've seen a student who had never been a Catholic or set foot in a Catholic Church give "the sign of the cross" as he exited an aircraft. Later, when questioning him about it, he stated repeatedly that he had never done it before and probably wouldn't have believed us had we not had video of it.

Law enforcement officers endure immense stress in the face of a known criminal who they're not sure is armed. Firefighters also experience great amounts of stress going into a burning building. Emergency medical technicians (EMTs) go through a lot of stress trying to save someone's life while also getting the victim extracted from a wrecked vehicle.

No matter what your profession as a tactical athlete, you cannot let stress win in situations where it can cause failure, thereby costing the lives of you and/or those around you. Your level of fitness is one way to combat stress. You owe it to yourself, your family, and to those you serve to maintain a high level of fitness, ensuring you will "win" and make it home.

I'll finish this chapter with one simple statement about something I believe. I'm not going to write about it; I'm just going to let you think about it: **Before the tactical athlete can be successful, I believe he/ she must first train from the inside out.**

2

A Growth Mindset for Fitness

If you've studied *growth* versus fixed mindset, you know that a growth mindset is one that allows you to be open to new ideas and thinking outside of the box. It also lets you know that you have the ability to do whatever you want. On the other hand, a fixed mindset says things like, "I'm just not good at exercise." For you to be at your best, you need a growth mindset. If you haven't researched growth versus fixed mindset, I would suggest looking up some of the material by Carol Dweck.

If you fall into the category of *tactical athlete*, your job and your life probably depend on your level of fitness. You need to maintain a high level of physical fitness to maintain your well-being and lifestyle. A computer can have the greatest software in the world, but if it doesn't have a power source, it's no good. You can have all the smarts in the world when it comes to your job in the tactical realm, but unless you have the level of fitness you need to perform and survive, again, it's no good. The Original Strength (OS) system will get you there. Understand that the things you'll learn in OS aren't *all* you need, but they are a large part of it. The RESETs and the principles you'll learn will greatly benefit you.

Understand that just because "celebrity A" says he or she uses a certain technique or program to get in shape, that doesn't mean it will work for you or that "celebrity A" is necessarily fit. Think outside the norms when it comes to fitness. Don't think that going into a gym, reading directions on a machine, and then doing the exercises will make you fit. Also, don't think you can look at someone and tell how fit that person is. Size doesn't equal strength. Don't get fixed into thinking that big muscles equal strength or fitness, and don't think that someone with a slight gut isn't strong or in shape. In my profession, I've seen plenty of people who weren't built like a bodybuilder or a marathon runner yet were in excellent shape.

Some of the things you're going to learn in the Original Strength system are a paradigm shift from fitness industry norms. My guess is that what you learn from OS you'll begin to hear more about as time goes and people catch on.

Functional Fitness

What do we mean when we say functional fitness? I would define it simply as follows:

Functional fitness is fitness that is applicable to the necessary skills *you* need in life.

The skills *you* need in life would include what you do daily in life, your job, and your hobbies.

All too often, people base their workouts on things like the bench press. That's fine if you're a lineman on a football team. On one of my deployments to the Middle East, I had a friend who was in the "400-Pound Bench Press Club," a program found in gyms on deployments for people to showcase their bench press prowess. In the same gym, they had a decent set of kettlebells of which I was one of the few people using them for things other than side bends. I was working my way up to what would be a max of a 95-pound kettlebell Turkish get-up (TGU) when the bench press folks became interested in what I was doing. I invited them down to learn and try TGUs. I started them out much like I learned at the RKC—that is, holding a water bottle in their hand. From there, we went to a 35-pound kettlebell. Zero out of three of these people in either the 300- or 400-Pound Bench Press Club could do a Turkish get-up with a measly 35-pound kettlebell. So, which move is more important for daily life? The bench press or the Turkish get-up?

I would encourage you to shape your workouts around exercises that you know will provide full-body, functional fitness. If you're a person who needs the bench press for that, then, by all means... enjoy. Just don't forget to tie everything together with other exercises.

Take a look at what you're doing in your current exercise routine, and adapt it to what you need. One example might be pull-ups. What is your hand position when doing them? If you fit into the tactical athlete category, you should probably be doing them with your palms facing away. In what real-world situation would you be doing a pull-up-like movement? Maybe climbing over a wall or into a window? In that case, your palms would be facing away.

Functional fitness for the tactical athlete is not one-size-fits-all either. If you're an infantryman in the military, you obviously need strength, but you also need a good deal of general endurance training. If you're on a prison system special response team, you probably need more power than endurance.

I don't want to discourage against setting strength goals, but I would also recommend looking at how your strength applies. If your goal is to squat 700 pounds, do you really need to? If you want to, that's fine, but understand the stress you are putting on your body to achieve that goal. Is it necessary? Or could you set a goal of 300 pounds that would fit more into the level you need for daily life and your profession?

One method might be to brainstorm and write down a list of what you do daily that requires any amount of fitness or movement. You could also make a list of what you want to be able to do. In what ways would your life be easier if you were stronger? Once you've done that, try to identify some exercises that fit with or simulate those tasks. Whatever your method, don't just exercise blindly without purpose.

Who Needs a Gym?

Let's discuss the confinements of a gym. What I'm mostly speaking of are the typical gyms that are crowded with machines and weightlifting equipment. By the way, just lifting weights does not equal fitness. Let's get that out of the way up front.

A big part of the Original Strength system is *restoration*, restoring our bodies to the way they were meant to be. We will go over the many benefits, but another way to achieve restoration is to just get out and do work. Get out in the open and play. Do your RESETS once you learn them out in open space, not in a gym. Weather permitting, find an open field or park to do your RESETS and space to crawl.

Gyms are full of machines designed to isolate body parts and help you train specific muscles while, at the same time, almost "guarding" other muscles from working. Some of these machines are gateways to overuse injuries and help you build imbalances and compensations in your body. Gym equipment can be counter-intuitive to building a strong foundation of true strength.

Understand I'm not saying gyms are bad. It's what you do in these gyms that can be bad. Understanding how to train for a strong foundation of reflexive stability and strength is key. You need a strong root system before you can grow truly strong.

Also, be wary of gyms set up for the latest trend in circuit training. Chiropractors and physical therapists everywhere are thankful for some of the latest fitness crazes as their businesses continue to grow as a result of them. Without a strong root system, some of the latest trends in circuit training can be detrimental to your health.

From bodybuilders to high-intensity circuit trainers, everyone can benefit greatly from OS.

So what's my point? Use gyms wisely. Train wisely. Understand that your movement and base reflexive strength needs to be firmly in place before you tackle bigger challenges. Just because someone is in the military and adheres to a regular physical training regimen doesn't mean the soldier is "good enough." Remember my story about "strong" guys attempting the Turkish get-up? A big bench press doesn't mean you're truly strong either.

With all of that said, yes, any of these forms of exercise or strength training can be good for you. You just need to have a good base or root system. Original Strength will help you get and maintain that base of strength. From bodybuilders to high-intensity circuit trainers, everyone can benefit greatly from OS.

So how can we know if our base reflexive strength is good enough? We'll show you some ways to determine that in a bit.

3

Introduction to Original Strength

This book is not meant to replace the "original" *Original Strength* or *Pressing Reset* books by Tim Anderson and Geoff Neupert. Some of the information here will be the same, but I recommend viewing this book as a companion book to *Original Strength* and *Pressing Reset*.

Original Strength is a system developed by Tim Anderson and Geoff Neupert to help you maintain or restore movement. Now, if you ask Tim, he will tell you God gave us our Original Strength and that he is just the messenger.

> You were made to be strong and move well at any age. You can regain and reclaim your Original Strength at any age. – Tim Anderson

OS is derived from studying how babies learn to move and develop strength as they grow. By mimicking some of the same movements a baby makes, we can restore our bodies' resilience and reflexive strength.

But you're already strong… right? Understand that just because you exercise or lift weights doesn't necessarily mean you have reflexive strength or have a strong foundation. Tying everything together and having a strong core is key. Original Strength will help you with that.

If you're working out to make yourself stronger but not tying your body together by building functional, reflexive strength, you are spinning your wheels. Do you really want a strong, mobile, and resilient body? Keep reading.

Brilliance in the Basics

I've done time behind a long gun and taught pistol marksmanship, so let's use those as examples. You can't be successful with hitting a target at 1,000 meters with a .308 rifle or at 50 meters with a pistol unless you have the basic fundamentals mastered. Notice I said "mastered," not perfected. I believe very few people ever *perfect* the basics, but you can *master* them with lots of hard work and practice. In anything you do, the basics have to be mastered before you can do advanced things well. If you're going to secure a team house in a foreign country, the basics are understanding the security considerations of a patrol base. I could go on with examples, but you get the point.

In a way, *Original Strength* is the basics. There are advanced parts of OS, but the RESETS are your basics or baseline.

The tree diagram below does a great job of providing a broad illustration of Original Strength. OS is your root system. With a strong root system, you can have a strong trunk that will allow you to conduct normal daily activities. Then, you have your branches, which could be thought of as your hobbies or extracurricular activities. Without the strong root system, the tree can't grow strong and branch out. Original Strength will give you a strong root system to prepare you for anything life throws at you

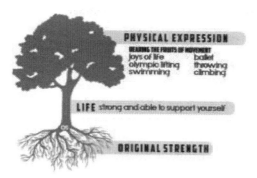

To help with explaining OS, I asked Tim to write some "OS truths." Here they are:

1. All of us were made to be strong throughout our entire lives.
2. Our bodies were not meant to be fragile.
3. The body was made to heal and repair itself.
4. We were designed to move.
5. Movement is the vehicle that is intended to build our brains, our nervous systems, our minds, and our bodies.
6. We were all pre-programmed with certain developmental movement patterns designed to make us strong and resilient.
7. We never outgrow or out-age our original movement program. The movements and patterns that made us strong as children are still the movements and patterns that can return our strength and keep us strong as adults.
8. Engaging in our original movement template is like pressing a "RESET button" in our nervous system. It can reboot and restore our original operating system, thus restoring reflexive connections throughout the brain and body and reestablishing reflexive strength.

9. Reflexive strength, your original strength, is the foundation for all movement.

10. Strength, health, and resiliency are all expressions of the body's natural design.

11. There are three keys to strength, health, and resiliency:

- We must breathe correctly. We should be "belly breathers" and not chest or neck breathers.
- We must move our heads. Where the head goes, the body will follow.
- We must engage in our gait pattern, moving our limbs contra-laterally in coordination with one another.

How do these "OS truths" relate to the tactical athlete? If you are one, you should have this answer already. Anyone who fits into the title of "tactical athlete" needs to be reflexively strong, mobile, and resilient as much as anyone. Being able to shoot, move, and communicate while also handling the effects of stress on the body are essential. You shouldn't strive to be able to just handle stress but to handle it well. Just as your brain has to be adaptable in tactical situations, so must your body. By the way, did I mention OS is great for the brain as well? We'll get into that later.

4

Do You Need OS?

So maybe you already have a normal fitness routine. You may wonder why you would need something as simplistic as Original Strength. Just because you do well with certain fitness routines or programs doesn't mean you necessarily have a strong foundation.

So we developed a simple, three-part test for you to gauge how much you need Original Strength. (Whether you test well or not, we still believe you will benefit from OS.)

This short test can be done anywhere you like, and it's self-paced. You will need some space in order to crawl, so outside may be the best option unless you have a large, open floor indoors. One thing to keep in mind is that you should do each part of the test "cold," not making repeated tries to complete them. This test was designed to see if you have good reflexive strength to perform your job and navigate through your daily life in "emergency" situations. This test is not to see how well you do after you've warmed up. For the tactical athlete, there are no "do-overs" in most of our jobs.

The Baseline Test

Part 1: Forward crawl

> 1. You will learn technique more later in the book, so for now, just crawl forward on your hands and feet with your head up and butt level or below your head.

2. Crawl forward for three minutes without rest in the aforementioned position. Oh, and keep your mouth closed while you breathe in and out through your nose.

Part 2: Weighted-front carry

1. Stand tall and hold an item at least 1/3 of your bodyweight at chest level three inches away from your body.
2. Walk 50 yards without rest.

Part 3: Contralateral one-arm, one-leg balance

1. Assume a natural pushup position. Your hands and feet should be no more than shoulder-width apart.
2. Lift your right arm and left leg at the same time, and balance for five seconds. Then, do the same with the opposite arm and leg.

You may think, "Why do I need to crawl?" I urge you to continue reading and continue working on it. The results will speak for themselves.

You may also think, "Why do I need to carry something in front of me when what I carry is always on my back?" If you do this, you will notice how your core will light up like a Christmas tree. This is reflexive strength in action.

You may also dismiss the third test, saying, "I just don't have good balance." Don't make this mistake. Good balance is crucial to good health and being able to respond when an emergency calls. Give this test a try and see what you discover.

So how did you do?

Even if you did well at those tests, and we hope you did, pressing RESET with Original Strength will still benefit you greatly. You'll be able to use the RESETS and then get into some of the advanced RESETS more quickly, such as the loaded crawling you'll learn about later.

If you had trouble with any or all of the tests, then you've got some work to do. Fear not. We have just what you need. Just keep reading. All of these tests and the results you had correlate with the state of your reflexive strength, your foundation of strength. This book aims to help you tie all of this information together as to tie your body together so you can become stronger and more resilient and improve your chances for success and always returning home.

5

OS RESETS

The *Original Strength* RESETS are the basis of the system. We are going to briefly go over the "Big 5" RESETS: breathing with the diaphragm, head control, rolling, rocking, and crawling/cross-crawling. I encourage you to purchase the Original Strength book, *Pressing RESET* in order to learn about them more in depth. *Pressing RESET* is the rewrite of the *Original Strength* title book.

Each RESET has regressions and progressions. The regressions are for those that may need something lighter, and the progressions are for those who need a little more. Note, however, that one man's regression may be another's progression.

The term *reset* is what these are all about. The idea is that, when done on a regular basis, they can reset your body to its original form and function. I recommend doing them once daily at a minimum. I also would prescribe "taking as needed." If you've done a long, strenuous physical training session such as a 12-mile foot march, then RESETS afterward are a good idea. After a long day of airborne operations (jumping out of airplanes) is another good time. The RESETS are great for anytime, from a long period of sitting to the end of a long day of physical training.

I do RESETS first thing in the morning, before and/or after working out, and at the end of the day. I may not do all of the Big 5, but I'll get some in. And again, I do them "as needed," such as after a long day of jumping and pulling jumpmaster duties.

The concept is simple: move. Movement gets your joints "oiled up" and your blood flowing. The RESETS activate your brain and get you charged up for whatever is on your agenda next.

During all RESETS, you should have your tongue resting on the roof of your mouth; this is where your tongue belongs. And, if you can, keep your mouth closed. This encourages your diaphragm to do its job. It is also one of the best ways to relieve stress that may be hiding in your mind as well as in your body.

Diaphragmatic Breathing

Diaphragmatic breathing is when you breathe the way you were born to breathe. This means pulling air down into "your belly" by using your diaphragm to fill your lungs up from the bottom to the top. This may seem like a very simple and useless exercise, but it is probably the most important thing you could ever do as this is foundational and critical to your overall health and performance, both mentally and physically.

Breathing with your diaphragm takes you from fight-or-flight mode and places you into rest-and-digest mode. For anyone in the military who deals with post-traumatic stress disorder (PTSD), breathing like this could literally be the "breath of life" as it helps to lower the hormonal stress responses caused by the various stresses of service in the military. This really can help you return to a state of "rest and digest" and "peace" mode.

Any of this sound familiar or useful? If you're a tactical athlete and have done any kind of weapons training, this either has been or should have been a tool in your kit. You may have heard it called *tactical breathing* as it's taught in some military courses. Utilizing tactical (diaphragmatic) breathing can be extremely useful for the tactical athlete. It can have benefits for shooting to high-stress engagements or negotiations.

When I was a young team leader and squad leader in the 82nd Airborne Division, I ran a lot. I've always been a pretty good runner, and I have a runner's build. Plus, with running around four days a week, I had no choice but to be good at it. There's also a part of being a leader in which you need to be able to lead from the front, so I always felt like I needed to be the fastest or, at least, one of the front runners in my unit. One thing my guys used to always comment about was how I was hardly ever out of breath after runs when they were sucking air hard. Of course, as the leader, I usually ran out front so they couldn't see me sucking air during the run. I had trained myself to slow my breathing and heartrate quickly so I could, at least, appear like I wasn't hurting after a hard run. What I know now is that I was simply switching back from *emergency breathing* up in my chest to *diaphragmatic* breathing down in my abdomen. That deeper and slower breathing allowed me to calm things down and appear collected as opposed to exhausted.

You should also have picked up on how this can help you as a tactical athlete when it comes to your training—specifically, training that involves shooting. We'll talk more about that later.

Breathing this way also makes you strong from the inside and center out. When you breathe with your diaphragm, you are strength training with your inner core muscles. It is the diaphragm that works with and coordinates with the muscles of the inner core, the deep muscles that protect and stabilize your spine, giving you a solid center. This allows your body to produce and transfer large amounts of force without getting injured. Yes, breathing makes you resilient and ready.

This is how you can remember how to breathe:

1. Lie on the floor in a comfortable position.
2. Try lying on your back with your knees bent and your feet flat on the floor.
3. Place your tongue on the roof of your mouth.
4. Breathe in and out through your nose while trying to pull air deep down into your belly.
5. Your belly should rise and fall before your chest does.

You will notice the first step in every RESET below is to "set your breathing" as described above. This reset is the RESET within all the other RESETS. Eventually, this will just come naturally, and you will simply do it without thought.

Head Control

Neck nods are so important because every single muscle in your body is reflexively attached to the movements of your head. Surely, you have heard the saying, "Where the head goes, the body will follow." This is evident in combatants. If you gain control of your opponent's head, you gain control of your opponent's body. This is also true with moving your own head. By simply moving your head around, you stimulate every single muscle in your body, and you sharpen your reflexes globally. You also keep your brain stimulated and alert, ready to receive input and command action.

Here are the steps to working on your head control:

1. Set your breathing.
2. Start on your hands and knees.
3. Sit back on your heels.
4. Tuck your chin into your chest with your eyes looking down (just as if you're about to exit an aircraft while in flight).
5. Look up at the ceiling, leading with your eyes, and look as far back as you can.
6. Repeat this process.

I recommend doing about 10 to 20 of these. As an addition, you can do the same thing side to side to grease up the neck even more. Experiment with these nods in different positions (e.g. resting on your forearms, hands and knees with butt not on heels, etc.).

Rolling

This one sounds simple but can actually be pretty complicated. Rolling helps to lubricate and repair the spine, and it also further connects the body from the inside out. It is a great way to restore your body while you also build reflexive strength. Rolling can be done in many different ways, but we will stick to segmental rolling in this book. The simple directions for this are to lay on the floor and roll from your front to your back and then from back to front. This is one I probably enjoy the most. I like getting a nice, quick, elongated stretch and then going right into rolling.

When doing segmental rolling, one of the keys is to use half your body at a time. You will only use your upper body to execute your rolls and then switch to using your lower body to roll.

Here's your step by step breakdown:

Back–to–front rolls (upper body)

> 1. Set your breathing.
> 2. Lay on your back completely outstretched and with your arms straight overhead.
> 3. Begin the roll with your eyes and head, then neck, and then reach across your body with your right arm. Reach as far as you can until you roll over to your belly. DO NOT USE YOUR LEGS.
> 4. One method to use on this roll is to tuck your chin toward your armpit as you roll.

Front-to-back rolls (upper body)

> 1. Lay on your belly in the same manner as you did on your back, completely outstretched.
> 2. Begin the roll with your eyes and head, then neck, and then reach back across your body with your right arm. Reach and continue as far as you can until you've rolled over. DO NOT USE YOUR LEGS.
> 3. You'll have to reach extra with your head on this one.

Back-to-front rolls (lower body)

> 1. Lie on your back completely outstretched and with your arms straight overhead.
> 2. Leading with your right leg, reach across with the leg until you roll over. DO NOT USE YOUR UPPER BODY.

Front-to-back rolls (lower body)

> 1. Lie on your front completely outstretched and with your arms straight overhead just as you did on your back.
> 2. Lead with your right leg, reaching back across your body until you roll over onto your back. DO NOT USE YOUR UPPER BODY.

Start/End Position on back

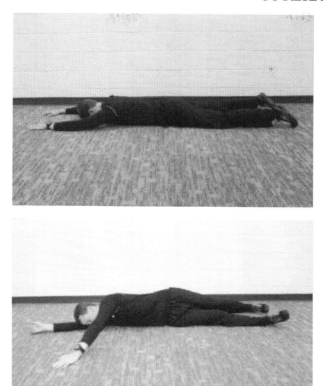

Upper body rolling back to front

With all these rolls, you should be able to do them fairly easily. At one point, I had trouble with upper-body segmental rolls to the right, so Tim had me put a pillow underneath my left shoulder to assist me. Eventually, I was able to do them easily without the pillow, so this is one method you might use if you have issues rolling in a certain direction.

As a general rule, I like to roll three times in each direction with both the upper and lower body. There are advanced rolls described in the *Original Strength* title book and in *Pressing RESET* that can be attempted and used once you're comfortable with segmental rolling and want to try something more challenging.

Upper body rolling front to back

Lower body rolling front to back

Rocking

Rocking is probably the most adaptable of all the RESETS next to cross-crawls, which we'll get to in a bit. Rocking is fairly self-explanatory. You simply rock back and forth. You can really get creative with this RESET once you've gotten the hang of it in its most basic form.

Also, along with cross-crawls, this one is the most accessible. You can easily hop down into a rocking position and knock them out...

although you may get some funny looks, depending on where you are at the time. Rocking feels great and will loosen up several joints: wrists, shoulders, hips, knees, and ankles. If you could only do one RESET prior to doing a full-body workout, I would recommend *rocking*.

So at this point, you may be wondering, "How do I do this rocking you speak of?" Well, here you go:

1. Set your breathing.
2. Start on your hands and knees with your hands directly below your shoulders and butt up with your legs, forming a 90-degree angle.
3. The tops of your feet should be on the ground with your feet flexed.
4. Hold your head and chest up erect.
5. Move your butt toward your feet until your butt touches your heels, or move back as far as you can without allowing your spine to bow.
6. Return to the starting position.

Rocking start position

At first, practice this slowly, and get comfortable with how it feels. You'll quickly see the benefits. Your keys are to keep breathing properly, keep your head and chest up, and use a full range of motion.

Once you're comfortable with this movement, there are several ways to progress it. You can change the position of your feet to having

Rocking down position (plantar-flexed feet)

Rocking down position (dorsi-flexed feet)

your toes flexed on the ground, having your toes pointed inward, or pointing your toes outward. You can also rock with your knees off the ground so that you're only on your hands and feet.

One example of how to progress the rock is to add a pushup. Sound interesting? Give it a try.

1. Set your breathing.
2. Start on your hands and knees, just as in a normal rock, with your head and chest up.

3. Move your butt to your feet the same as in a normal rock.
4. When you return to the start position, carry yourself past it, and do a pushup.
5. Repeat.

Rocking pushup start position

Rocking pushup back position

Do this slowly at first, and play with it. Figure out your hand positioning. If this move is difficult, push your hands out more forward than normal in the starting position, and then attempt it again. It should be slightly easier. If you feel like challenging yourself, inch your hands back as you do it. This will change your leverage, and the

Rocking pushup down position

pushup will get harder. Want even more of a challenge? Do it with your knees off the ground.

Crawling

Crawling is the granddaddy of all RESETS. Crawling is a solid way to "train the X" and to tie your body together. Crawling will really test your core strength and reflexive stability. When you're crawling, you have at least four points of contact with the ground, so your proprioceptors in your hands and feet are getting instant feedback from the ground or whatever surface you're using.

When you crawl, make sure you're using contralateral movement—that is, your opposite limbs are moving in unison. Your left hand should reach forward as your right leg comes up and vice versa. So when you think about this, it's easy to see how crawling ties your body together and can really make you strong.

Crawling is simple, and everyone has most likely done it at some point. This is how you built strength as a baby and can be how you continue to build strength. Maybe crawling sounds too easy for you? Don't worry; stay tuned, and we'll make sure you're challenged. What about crawling a mile? Yep, we'll get to that later. Really want to build strength? Crawl backward up a hill. Throw your gear on, and crawl. Or how about dragging chains? Again, we'll get to that later. We have to crawl before we walk... or, crawl before we... you get the point. We're only going to look at three different styles of crawling in this book: the baby crawl, the leopard crawl, and the spider-man crawl.

Key protocols to crawling in any position:

1. Set your breathing
2. Keep your head and chest up erect
3. Move your limbs contra-laterally
4. Keep your natural lumbar curve (flat back) with your butt lower than your head

Baby crawling

- This crawl is to be done on your hands and knees.
- Follow all other protocols to crawling.

Don't underestimate this crawl. It's a great, low-impact RESET. If for some reason you're not feeling the other crawls, this one is great. If you have any sort of injury, this one could be beneficial as well. This is also a good start to working on your coordination. Some folks have trouble with the contralateral movement at first. Start out with this crawl, and progress from there.

Leopard crawling

- You'll only be on your hands and feet with this crawl.

- Your knees should track inside your elbows.
- Follow all other protocols for crawling.

This crawl is considered a step up from the baby crawl, but it's not quite as hard as the spiderman crawl. The leopard crawl can be quite challenging as well though. Once you're comfortable with the normal forward leopard crawl, try playing with it by crawling backward as well as side to side.

I've found the leopard crawl will test your leg strength more so than the spiderman crawl, which tests your core strength.

Spiderman crawling

- Use only your hands and feet with this crawl.
- Your knees will track outside your elbows.
- Follow all other protocols for crawling.

Here it is, the king of the crawls. The spiderman crawl is what I recommend working up to. However, you may find that other crawls are more challenging than the spiderman crawl. That just most likely means you've found a weak spot in your overall core and reflexive strength.

Play with all of these crawls. Try them forward, backward, and sideways. Try crawling in a circle or in a figure-8 pattern. Be adaptable and think outside the box.

The crawls described here can be done in short order as RESETS. You can use them as part of your RESET order, or you can build on crawling and use it for building strength. We'll get to that in another chapter.

Cross-crawls

- Set your breathing.
- Touch with your opposite limbs (i.e. hands, forearm, or elbow should touch opposite knee or thigh)
- If you're limited in your movement due to injury, adapt these to your level of mobility

Cross-crawls are like regular crawls as they offer similar neurological results similar to crawling. They are similar but a little different. We're not going to go deep here, but cross-crawls are beneficial to the brain. This goes back to "training the X." Again, I suggest doing some research and picking up the *Pressing RESET* book if you want to learn more. Here, we're just going to get you familiar with them as a highly adaptable RESET.

Bruce Lee said, "Be water, my friends." Cross-crawls are the "water" of the RESETS. You can do them anywhere, from lying or sitting on the floor to standing to while running or skipping. Simply touch your opposite limbs. This can be done with your hand, forearm, or elbow touching to the opposite knee or thigh.

You can even do these from the push-up position. As long as you know the keys, you can "be water" and adapt cross-crawls to do them in whatever environment you're in or make them as difficult as you want.

My typical way of doing these is to stand and put my fingertips behind my ears while touching my opposing elbow and knee. You should try to pay attention to how symmetrical your moves are. This could show you how you may be limited in mobility from side to side.

So these are the "Big Five" RESETS. I suggest practicing each one and getting comfortable with them. One thing I usually tell people with any training is to not "outrun your headlights." Use that advice here, and don't try to progress faster than you're capable. If you have trouble with some of the advanced crawls, then baby crawl. It's okay. Original Strength is about building a solid foundation to grow on. You'll likely not reach your full potential until you get that foundation "bricked in," brick by brick.

Enjoy!

6

The Wonderful World of Crawling

The title of this chapter can be misleading. While crawling is wonderful, as you progress and challenge yourself, it can be very un-wonderful. It becomes more and more challenging as you start progressing by adding weight and dragging things or by going for longer distances and times. However, from the standpoint of the benefits it has, it is wonderful.

We build muscle strength by keeping our muscles under tension. Right? What better way to do that than to be on "all fours" under tension while crawling around? Through reflexive tension (reflexive strength), crawling ties the body together and sharpens the reflexes. It also restores the nervous system, allowing you to train hard without tearing your body down.

In this chapter, we're going to explore several ways to crawl by increasing the tension on your muscles through time, distance, direction, and by adding weight—either by wearing it or pulling it.

While I am responsible for some of the techniques (aka. torture) here, most of it was developed by John Brookfield and Tim Anderson. They have a great training series called *Beyond Bodyweight Training* that I highly recommend. You can find more information about it on the Original Strength website.

Tips and Disclaimers

The disclaimer here is to take things easy, especially when you're wanting to crawl for longer times or distances. Your hands, wrists, and tendons may need some time to adjust. I recommend counter-flexing your wrists as you are crawling and getting used to it. That is, flex

41

them back down toward your forearm as they will spend a lot of time extended in the opposite direction as you crawl.

I also recommend having some gloves handy. This is mostly for safety as you crawl on various types of terrain. It's very sandy where I do most of my crawling currently, so that can wear on your skin quickly, as can concrete. It's also just a good idea because of any small, sharp objects you may encounter. Our hands are pretty important, and suffering from a hand injury that could have been avoided isn't much fun. You can find inexpensive gloves in multi-packs at your local department store.

As you get used to crawling, it will make you sore, but you will find that you recover quickly. You may be surprised to find just how quickly you recover and can get back at it. You may also be surprised to have muscle soreness in places where you haven't felt soreness before! Crawling has a way of filling in the nooks and crannies of your foundation. If you have any weak points, crawling will shore them up.

If you find yourself getting dizzy with some of these variations, don't worry. That's just your vestibular system working. Take it easy until you've adapted. If it's not your vestibular system that's the problem... drink water!

Don't forget the key protocols when doing any crawling:

- Keep your mouth closed, set your breathing, and breathe through your nose.
- Keep your head and chest up and erect.
- Move your limbs contra-laterally. (Opposing limbs should move together.)
- Maintain your natural lumbar curve (flat back) with your butt held lower than your head.

Axis crawling

The first crawling variation we'll get into here is axis crawling. This is simply crawling in a circle, using your own bodyweight. Imagine you had a skewer right through your mid-section (wonderful thought) and that you were rotating around it. That's axis crawling.

This method of crawling is great if you lack space as it doesn't take up much room. So if you're deployed somewhere or held to a confined space because of mission requirements, this is something that can be beneficial to have in your kit.

With this crawl, as I said earlier, you're simply going in a circle. Keep your limbs moving contra-laterally, which may take some getting used to. I recommend doing this one with a timer so you will get an equal amount of time turning in one direction and then back in the other direction.

This particular crawl is great because it strengthens your vestibular system due to the spinning and because it builds coordination. Again, the sharper your vestibular system, the sharper you are.

Lateral crawling

Crawling laterally is great upper-body work. It truly works the whole body, but it will also work your upper body in much the same way as a butterfly machine in a "box gym" will... only better. And, it's functional.

There's not much to explain with this. Just use the same protocols, and go sideways. Move your limbs contra-laterally, but don't cross them over. When your hands are together, your feet should be apart. Be prepared to find your hips on this one. It will wake them up if you don't use them much.

I do lateral crawling anywhere but have found it great to do somewhere like a football field where you have a straight line to follow. As you're getting used to this one, you may notice you have trouble moving contra-laterally or staying straight. You may also notice you can crawl laterally in one direction better than you can in the other direction. This is all perfectly normal. Just take it easy and practice the movement rather than trying to work hard. This is how you learn from your movement.

Backward crawling

Sounds easy. Right? Wrong. Backward crawling will challenge your upper body. This one definitely takes some getting used to. It may take several practice sessions before you're able to work out with this one. Just take it easy, and explore it.

The wild thing about this crawl is that the brain essentially reverses the body. For example, your hips will work more like your shoulders, and your toes will work more like your fingers. The same happens with your arms. They begin acting more like your legs.

One of the best ways to experience this is to find two objects you can crawl backward around in a figure-8 pattern. John Brookfield calls this the "infinity crawl." As you attempt to turn and find your way around the objects, you'll feel how differently your body works.

Infinity Crawl

If you really want to challenge yourself, get some elevation in your life. Find a hill, and crawl backward up it. Without a doubt, this is the apex of all bodyweight crawling drills. Nothing is harder to do, and nothing will tie your body together quite like this will. You can't help but become strong when you crawl backward up a hill.

Be careful with this one. I've seen folks face or elbow plant hard doing this one with a little moisture on the grass. During one morning physical training session, we ended up looking for a wedding ring after this one as well. Moral of the story: Secure your gear.

You can do the backward crawl by using any of the forward-crawl techniques already described in the chapter about the RESETS. When you practice this crawl, I recommend starting with the baby crawl first. Once you have the hang of that, move to the leopard crawl and then on to the spider-man crawl.

Crawling-workout parameters

You may be wondering how fast to go and for what duration. Let's dive deeper into how to use these different crawling methods in your workouts.

First, let's talk about time and distance. You can set your goal to accomplish one or both, but make sure you start in small chunks. If you want to go for a certain amount of time, say 10 minutes, don't worry about doing that non-stop... yet. Use your timer, and when you stop for a break, stop your timer. See how you progress by tracking how long you can crawl without stopping. By the way, 10 minutes of crawling is somewhat of a standard I typically encourage people to shoot for.

If you choose to go for distance, I encourage you to keep track of how far you go without stopping each time. That way, you can see how much you progress as you go. If you have access to one, a football field makes this pretty easy to do.

Again, set manageable goals. If you choose to progress in both distance and duration, have fun. This can be really challenging. As an initial goal, aim to crawl 1/4 mile in 15 minutes.

Loaded crawling

As if crawling with bodyweight alone isn't challenging enough, let's add some weight. Once you've built a base by being able to execute the crawls properly, you can start thinking about adding a load. Adding a load to the crawls will cement them and build some serious power. There are several ways you can add a load, and we'll explore some of them here.

The first method should be all too familiar to those who consider themselves tactical athletes: a weighted vest. Most of you should have, or have access to, some sort of body armor or plate carrier. Ensure you have one that fits properly and is somewhat comfortable. As you try this method, you'll have to experiment with whatever you use. There are weight vests specifically for exercise you can buy, but it's a good idea just to use the kit you have. Avoid having your vest/carrier too tight as it will restrict your breathing.

Many moons ago, getting on all fours and crawling was one thing I would do to ensure my gear was solid. If you have all your pouches and things such as magazines in place, you'll quickly find out if anything is going to shake loose or fall out. This is another way crawling can be beneficial and is another way to "train like you fight."

As with anything, take it easy at first when you add weight with something such as a vest. This can put quite a strain on your lower back if you're not used to it, so work your way up to it. Scale it, and don't try to be a hero your first day.

The second way to load up your crawls is by dragging things like chains or sleds. To drag things, I used to use a rigger's belt. This works okay but can wear on your hips with heavier weight as well as be tough on your lower back.

There are different ways to fashion straps to use, but the method I recommend far and away is to go to the Original Strength website and check out the "Infinity Strap." It's a strap developed just for OS and is extremely versatile for loaded crawling. I'm not just saying this to sell straps for OS—I bought my own and get no commission on this—but I'm saying this because it's easily the best method I've found.

There's also the OS Loop that was developed by a professional football strength and conditioning coach. It's as simple as the name; it's a loop. However, it's a great and versatile tool for pulling weight.

Photo ©Jebb Graff

Photo ©Jebb Graff

John Brookfield has done some world-record pulls you can read about on his website or by just giving him a "google." If you're a man of mighty feats of strength like John, how might you get a harness strong enough to do things like pulling a 40,000-pound truck? You go to someone who makes leather harnesses for horses. Yep. Below is a picture of John's harness. He has set a few world records while wearing this harness as he dragged a 40,000-pound truck for a mile.

Another way to drag chains would be from each limb. This is awfully wonderful. If you can find a way to attach chains to your wrists or ankles, you can add a new dimension to your crawls. Chains work best here because they offer a "smooth drag." They won't get bound up or hung on any impediments on the ground. To know how special this crawl is, you have to experience it. Words don't really do it any justice.

I rigged this crawl up by using a set of padded lifting straps I got at a local sporting goods store. I just took them to one of the many sew shops you find in a military town and had the strap portions sewn up to form a loop so I could attach the chains with a carabiner.

You're now probably wondering what to drag. You can be creative, but again, my recommended option is chains. Chains are also sold on the OS website, but you can also pick up some chains at most hardware stores. Chains that are long will have more surface area dragging on the ground, therefore providing more resistance. I went the route of a local home improvement store, and I had three lengths cut at about 15 feet each. If you want to add more weight, you can always add more chain, or you can add other items. For extra weight to drag, I added kettlebells plus a couple of old discs from a brake job I had done. It's all about drag and friction.

When it comes to training, chains can also be used for several things other than dragging. Again, I highly recommend taking one of John Brookfield's *Beyond Bodyweight Training* workshops. John has a way of taking simple implements and teaching you how to use them to develop a powerful body and mind. John also has some great books out there on grip strength as well, so I encourage you to read his books.

Using something such as a vest will really challenge your core, but dragging things will challenge your whole body. One difference is that using a weighted vest will be more consistent in how it challenges you. The vest bears down on you; it tries to crush you.

Dragging weight pulls through you and tries to break your posture. The body's reflexive response to this is where real strength is born. Dragging loads will significantly strengthen your reflexive postural muscles, thus strengthening your whole body. The better posture you have, the better you will perform and adapt. Dragging loads also changes from crawl to crawl, depending on which crawl you use and what type of terrain you might be crawling on.

For example, crawling forward while dragging a significant amount of weight is much like doing a bunch of single-leg presses in a row. It builds strong thighs and hips and will blow your legs up! But crawling backward while dragging a load builds amazingly strong, resilient shoulders. It also strengthens your obliques better than any "core" workout you have ever done or ever will do.

While under a load, you can crawl using any of the different crawling methods described in this book. The axis crawl will only lend itself to the weight vest or other load that is placed directly on the body. It is kind of hard to drag a load when you are crawling in circles and going nowhere.

Again, take it easy, and learn from your body. Get some practice in and make sure you're fully capable of doing the crawls properly before adding a load. You need to have a strong base before you start adding much weight. But once you have that base, have fun and experiment with the crawls while weighted. You'll quickly find that some are more special than others. For instance, if you thought backward crawls were special with just body weight, try dragging 100 pounds of chain backward. That's truly special and almost indescribable.

By this point, you're probably ready to get out there and challenge yourself with some of these crawls, unloaded and then loaded. If you don't already see, you will eventually see how powerful crawling is for the tactical athlete. It will tie you together, and you'll become stronger than ever. I guarantee you will look and feel better when you train by carrying your gear as you utilize your reflexive strength.

7

OS for Marksmanship

As you've read, Original Strength has many benefits. Among those benefits is enhanced marksmanship. The majority of the people who consider themselves tactical athletes have a profession that involves carrying a weapon. Whether you carry a weapon for offensive, defensive, or competitive applications, OS can benefit you.

You probably know that studies show the better shape you're in, the better your ability to handle stress. In any application of firearms I listed above, you're going to have stress. One key to being a good marksman—as well as being able to handle stress—is good breathing. When shooting, remember that the first step of all the RESETS is to "set your breathing." Diaphragmatic breathing is beneficial for calming you and getting your heart rate down. This will ultimately give you better control over your motor functions, and as you probably know, one of the fundamentals of good marksmanship is good breathing.

I've found breathing to be the most beneficial of the RESETS, but I highly suggest using the others as well. My typical "go-to" RESETS on the range are diaphragmatic breathing, standing cross-crawls, and standing head nods. I also like rocking if the space and safety restrictions allow it on the range. I usually do my head nods in the rocking position if I can get rocks in. I use these RESETS as I get warmed up and will hit them quickly before a drill if I have the time. Between stages at a competition is a great time as well.

RESETS on the Range

- Breathing
- Standing cross-crawls
- Standing head nods
- Rocking (if space and safety permitted)

An extra time to get in your RESETS is when you get frustrated. If I'm having a bad day or not shooting well, I'll take a break and do some RESETS. It's the best thing I've found to help get out of a slump. If the RESETS don't help you get out of the slump, my advice is to pack up and do it another day. There's benefit in knowing when to call it quits before you hurt your confidence.

The OS System, if done regularly, will benefit you as a shooter as well. The benefits of the reflexive strength you will gain from crawling will pay dividends on the range, in the streets, or wherever you may be called to use your skills. All the benefits spoken of earlier in the book with contralateral movement will translate to your shooting skill.

Before using any firearms, ensure that you are properly trained in the use of that firearm, that you have a safe environment for shooting (preferably a shooting range), and that you understand the firearm safety rules. Know how to operate your particular firearm properly, and ensure that it is safe to shoot. Always treat all guns as if they are loaded. If you are new to shooting firearms, please get some training from a reputable instructor first.

Firearms Safety Rules

- The firearm is always loaded.
- Never point the firearm at something you aren't willing to destroy.
- Keep your finger off and away from the trigger until you are ready to shoot.
- Know your target and what is beyond it.

To test this, I developed an Original Strength "Shooting Test." Albeit unscientific, I put together some handgun shooting drills that I believed I could get results from. I shot the test for the first time in the spring. The idea was that, through the summer, I would train mainly using the Original Strength System and then shoot the test again toward the end of summer to determine if I improved.

During that time, my weekly routine looked like this:

- **Mondays:** Light crawling, loaded and unloaded
- **Tuesdays:** Run
- **Wednesdays:** Heavy-loaded crawling using various techniques
- **Thursdays:** Circuit and high-intensity training (varied)
- **Fridays:** Long crawls for distance

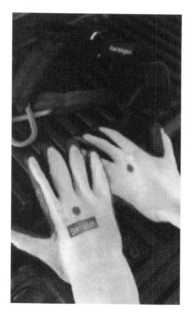

That may not be as detailed of a plan as some people would like, but that's how I like to manage my workouts. I like to keep fine details out, at times, so that I can have some freedom to play around or to adapt my workout to how I feel or my schedule.

As I stated before, I use gloves when crawling. An additional thing thing I did to help me work on my hand-eye coordination was to put a red dot on the knuckle of the middle finger on each of my hands. When crawling, I would take four "steps," keying in on the red dot of each hand as I planted it forward. I didn't do this during the entire crawl but ensured I did it for a bit each session. I can't tell you whether I experienced great results directly from that, but I do know there are similar drills that have been claimed to work.

I can tell you, however, that crawling is where humans develop hand-eye coordination and visual depth perception. This worked for us as children, and it can work for us as adults. My theory was *why not try it?*

I decided to use the handgun to conduct this test because that was the platform I needed to work on the most. So, as I stated before, there were several months between tests. I did one in April of 2015 and did the retest in September of 2015. In the time between tests, I only shot my handgun live a few times and only did dry fire at a maintenance level. I wanted the OS-geared workout plan to drive whatever improvement I might see by the second test, so I didn't do anything to improve my handgun skills between tests.

The test is done mainly from 10 yards away from the target. The target used was the only variable (except weather) from the test to retest. For the test, I used a larger steel plate that measured about 18"x12". The target I used on the retest was an RSR Steel, "ready to ship" target that had an A/B zone strike face of an IPSC target, measuring 10"x20". In other words, I was working with a smaller target for the retest. For both tests, I used the same setup and even wore the same shirt. The position from which I started the tests was the "surrender" position—that is, with hands up around neck level. I figured, with the movement this would allow for drawing the pistol, it would work better for these purposes instead of keeping my hands by my side. For this test, only hits count.

If you miss, that event has to be shot again. The "score" here is your time. Because I was using this test to judge how OS would help shooting, I wanted to use time only. While I'm certain using the RESETS on the range can help with accuracy, there are too many variables for me to test that. So again, you need to get all hits for the test to count, but your time is what your score is. So the implied task here is that you need a good shot timer. I shot each test three times and took my best time to help eliminate any "bad runs" that might hurt my ability to see accurately if the test worked.

Here's the breakdown of the test:

1. **Draw, and fire one round:** Begin 10 yards away in the surrender position. On the beep of the timer, draw, and fire one round.

2. **Shoot from behind a barricade to the right:** From 10 yards away, start from the surrender position with your hands on the barrier. On the beep of the timer, draw, and fire around the right side of the barrier. I used two stacked 50 gallon drums for this.

3. **Shoot from behind a barricade to the left:** From 10 yards away, start from the surrender position with your hands on the barrier. On the beep of the timer, draw, and fire around the left side of the barrier.

4. **Reload:** From 10 yards away, start from the surrender position. On the beep of the timer, draw, and fire two

rounds. Reload. Then, fire two rounds again. You will need all hits for the time to count.

5. **Shoot and move:** For this test, start from 20 yards away. You'll need three magazines with two rounds each, and you'll need to have the 10-yard line marked. On the beep of the timer, draw, and begin firing. As soon as you fire the first round, begin walking toward the 10-yard line. Walk and shoot from the 20 to the 10, firing six rounds total, two rounds per mag. There will be two mag changes in this string of fire.

6. **Stress test:** To start this one, you will need your handgun holstered, and I recommend having at least two full magazines. You will need to have the 10-, 15-, and 20-yard lines marked. Start at the target, facing away from the target and backstop. On the beep of the timer, do 20 burpees, the kind where you do a pushup. Once complete, move to the 10-yard line, draw your handgun, and get two hits. Then, move to the 15 and get two hits. Move to the 20 and get two hits. Then, do the same thing back to the 15 and 10. You will need a total of 10 hits, but it's okay if you miss. You just need to make those hits up so that you will get 10 total hits, two at each stop.

Below is the table that shows my times. These aren't blazing times, and some of the retest times aren't amazingly faster. But considering how little training I got in between the two tests, these improvements are great. I'm no speed demon, but if you're close to these times, you're doing pretty good.

Event	Test (03APR15)	Retest (02SEP15)
Draw and Fire One Round (10yds)	1.25 seconds	1.21 seconds
Behind 6ft Barricade, shoot to the right (10yds)	1.67 seconds	1.63 seconds
Behind 6ft Barricade, shoot to the left (10yds)	1.78 seconds	1.71 seconds
Draw, Fire 2 Rounds, Reload, Fire 2 Rounds (10yds)	5.36 seconds	5.20 seconds
Shoot and Move, 20yds to 10yds w/2 Reloads	13.73 seconds	12.65 seconds
Stress Test - 20 Burpees at the target, then move to the 10, 15, 20, 15, 10 getting 2 hits at each position	109.65 seconds	94.14 seconds

You'll notice the biggest improvements were in the tests that were the most physical and involved the most movement. Coincidence? I think not. My conclusion from this test is that using OS in your training absolutely does help. I would imagine, if I had set up some more dynamic drills that resemble competition-type stages, I would probably have experienced great results from that training as well.

These drills are just good tests of your abilities as a shooter as well. If you want to try these, always record your data to track your progress. One thing I learned from Mike Seeklander of Shooting Performance is the importance of recording your data in order to see how much you improve and to determine what you need to do to improve. Mike recommends recording very detailed data, everything from the gear you used and the weather to how you shot, of course.

I recommend going out and trying this test. Feel free to modify it however you like, or use a different platform such as an AR-15. Just make sure that, if you're going to do what I did, you try to keep the test and retest exactly the same. Modify the drills if you need to—these are definitely adaptable—but if you change much, I would recommend keeping in the shooting and moving as well as the stress-shoot portion.

If you're going to be a good shooter—whether it be for your job, for competition, or just for self-defense purposes—there are benefits to exercising regularly and being in shape. There are added benefits in having Original Strength be that means of getting in or maintaining optimal physical condition as we've discussed in this chapter and throughout this book.

Gear Used during my Test Shoots

- Smith and Wesson M&P9 full size
- 124gr 9mm ammunition (loaded myself)
- Safariland Model 5198 Paddle Holster
- 3x HSGI Pistol Tacos with Raven Concealment Systems Moduloader belt attachment
- Orion Filters Ballistic Eyewear
- CED 7000 Shot Timer

8

OS for the Warrior's Mind

Strength isn't always about muscles.

Throughout history, many technological advancements have occurred during times of war. During the Global War on Terror, many advancements have come from trying to better outfit our warriors headed to foreign lands as well as to help our guardians protect our citizens here at home. One thing that has remained constant is that the greatest tool available is the mind. So, as much as we worry about our bodies, we should also exercise our brains.

Movement is the vehicle that develops the brain. The body's design is very "chicken and egg"—that is, you need a brain to move, and you need movement to build your brain. One of the very first systems to develop in your body is the vestibular system (your balance system). It is fully developed five months after conception. All the movement and stimulus your body generates and receives becomes information that is routed through your vestibular system. It is this information that helps to build efficient neural connections and pathways in your brain. When there is a lack of information, these pathways weaken and even fade away, in a sense, starving your brain. It is movement that nourishes and grows a healthy brain.

There are specific movements that feed the brain well. The OS RESETS build efficient neural pathways that tie both hemispheres of the brain together. The more you engage in these RESETS, the more efficient the brain becomes at communicating in itself and throughout the body. A healthy, efficient brain creates a healthy, efficiently moving body. And a healthy, efficiently moving body keeps and sustains a healthy, efficient brain. It is very "chicken and egg."

This is of extreme importance for the tactical athlete because a healthy brain is also a brain that can focus, think, solve problems, overcome challenges, and even overcome emotions. A healthy brain is a necessity for a healthy mind. Again, this is very "chicken and egg." Your mind, the way you think, can even create and shape your brain much like movement does!

When the stress of the warrior's life has reached the level of life and death, decisions and actions must be made. Having a sound mind is of the utmost importance. Movement, "pressing RESET," is one way to achieve and create a sound mind via building a resilient, healthy brain.

There are other benefits to moving the way we were created to move. It can refresh the nervous system, lower stress, and soothe the emotions. For example, just the simple act of diaphragmatic breathing, breathing properly, can take the body from the "fight-or-flight" mode to the "rest-and-digest" mode. This, alone, can have huge implications for the recovery of a hardened warrior. Being able to live in rest-and-digest mode could allow for good, restorative sleep as well as proper adrenal hormone balance. Fight-or-flight mode should be reserved for emergencies, not everyday life. When one is able to live at rest and at peace, he cannot suffer from stress disorders.

Having said all of this, the movement and RESETS of Original Strength can pay great dividends in whatever your duties are as a "tactical athlete," whether in military, law enforcement, firefighting, or whatever your job is. The other benefit is in your daily life. The job responsibilities of many tactical athletes can lead stressful and trauma-filled lives. This can mean certain things in daily life can bring you anxiety or make you uncomfortable.

In the case of the military and the last more than a decade of conflict, a large percentage of us have experienced some stressful or horrific things. The RESETS of Original Strength can work as positive coping mechanisms. If you're experiencing anxiety over something and you realize it, take a few minutes to relax into your RESETS. Set your breathing, and get some movement in. This will work wonders for you in many different situations. Use the RESETS as your tool.

9

The One-Mile Crawl

God who arms me with strength and keeps my way secure.
—Psalm 18:32

Tim Anderson was the first to do the mile-long crawl, and as long as Tim and I have known each other, I've wanted to take a shot at his achievements. It's been harder to do since Tim became a full-time coach, but I like being challenged. He doesn't challenge me directly; I just use him to set my own bar for certain things. So when I saw that he did a one-mile crawl, which you can see on YouTube, I knew I had to try it.

Famous last words: "I can do that." Doing a one-mile spiderman crawl may not sound like a very daunting task, but it is. It's also one thing just to complete it, but to keep good form while doing it is taking it to another level. These are truths I would learn the hard way as I took on this task.

When I began, it was hard to crawl for 10 minutes without stopping, so how on earth was I going to crawl for an entire mile without stopping? That's right. No stopping and no breaks. So if you decide to take on this challenge, you may feel like it's unachievable. It may seem impossible, but it's not... not for someone "fearfully and wonderfully made" like you.

Let's talk about the crawl.

As I write this, it's August 28th of 2015, the day I completed the one-mile crawl. I decided to go for it and started training around May of 2015. Prior to that, I had crawled some but more for RESET purposes than for endurance or strength-building. Learning from Tim and John how to crawl and get strong helped to spearhead this effort.

So I decided that I would do various crawls on Mondays and Wednesdays and then go for distance on Fridays. My various crawls usually consisted of all the different methods and using my infinity strap to drag around 60 pounds of chain.

When I started trying for distance, I used a quarter-mile as a benchmark. That was a tough goal to start with, making it hard to see how I would manage to make it an entire mile. I then moved up to crawling a half-mile but took breaks as needed. By early July, I had worked up to crawling half-mile without stopping, so I then progressed to doing the half-mile before taking a break and then continuing on to three-quarters of a mile with breaks. During that last quarter-mile, I took several breaks as I was usually pretty tired at that point.

In mid-July, I had to go out to the field for training for a couple of weeks, which set me back on my training. At 37 years old, I don't bounce back after two weeks off like I used to. I also went on leave, so after the field and while home, I had to work my way back up. While back home on leave, I used my old football field for crawling. By the way, the grass back in Tennessee was much better than the grass-and-sand mix out here in North Carolina. I didn't even use gloves back in Tennessee. There, I only did a half-mile crawl but continued by using various other crawls.

Now back at Fort Bragg and realizing the time-frame in which I wanted to get this book completed, I needed to get after it. If I was going to get this book out on time, I needed to get this crawl done so I could write about it. I made the decision that I would just have to gut it out and make it happen.

That brings me to today, the day of the crawl. I decided the night before that I would get up early, say a prayer, and see what I could do. There's a good saying for times like this: "Let go and let God." It was about 70 degrees outside and dark, so it was pretty nice. I like working in the dark. I get inspired by the statement, "Putting in work in the dark," which is an exhortation to do good work even when no one is watching. I parked my truck in the usual spot behind my work, chalked my hands up, threw my gloves on, and got to it.

During the crawl, I knew one lap would be around a half-mile, so I vowed not to look at my watch for the distance until after that. The first time I looked at my watch was at .61 miles. That gave me confidence because I had never crawled that far without stopping. That was a good point to take a look at the watch because I had just come up a hill.

The next time I looked, my distance was at .75 miles, and I knew for sure at that point that I had it made. At around .81 miles, something popped in my wrist and sent a sharp pain up my arm. It scared me, but I just lifted that arm, shook it out, and powered through. That last quarter-mile was brutal, but I pushed through. By this time, the sun was up, and there were some other folks out doing physical training. I had started crawling at 0545 in the morning, and almost 50 minutes later, I was done.

I wanted a much faster time, but considering the amount of train-up time I had taken, I was just happy to have completed it.

The picture below isn't the best as my phone screen was broken and nearly unreadable when I took this. The second picture is a screenshot from the program my watch uses when downloading the information from my workouts.

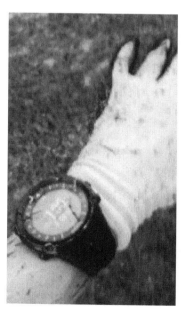

For me, the hardest thing about crawling that far is the mental challenge. Physically, it's tough, but I liken it to something like a 12-mile road march. It sucks, but you just push through. Being on all fours for that long when you're smoked and tired is extremely tough on the mind. There were times during the training when I would stand up, but then, I wouldn't be sure why I had stood up. Your brain is telling you the entire time that your body is tired and this hurts. "Stand up!" your body yells at you.

I'm sure my form wasn't as pretty as Tim's was, but past three-quarters of a mile, I was more in survival mode, and perfect form went out the window. I was able to maintain the basics such as keeping my butt below my head, but it was tough. There's no video of mine because I did it on a whim, and no cameramen were available at 0500 that morning. I'm extremely glad to have completed this challenge and, for now, to be one of only two OS'ers who have done it.

Oh, and you might ask how I doubled the distance I was able to crawl without stopping in just a couple of weeks. That can be explained right here in this verse…

> It is I can do all things through Christ who strengthens me.
> —Philippians 4:13

Side Note: Along with some other senior folks in my unit, I was blessed with the opportunity to speak to the Philadelphia

Eagles' rookies during one of their training camps. We were taking questions, and one of them asked how we continued on when things were so hard and when it felt like we didn't have any more to give. He was speaking about physical challenges, of course. Frankly, that's a question I don't even know truly how to answer. The answer is that you just don't quit. So I used the example of working on my goal of a one-mile crawl and how challenging it was with my brain just telling me to get up. But I had my goal in mind and wouldn't get up.

The looks and opened mouths I got when saying I wanted to crawl a mile were priceless. It caught me by surprise to get such a rise out of these guys about wanting to do that. I believe I heard the word "crazy" uttered in the group. Yep... It was crazy, but I didn't quit.

10

RESET Flows

In this chapter, I'm going to list some examples of RESET flows I use. Some of these will be abbreviated to allow for short breaks, but understand that I always recommend executing the "Big Five" when you have the time and space. I also recommend starting your day with at least a five-minute RESET flow and doing it again toward the end of your day.

Please note that these are just RESETS and not a complete workout. Think of using these more like warm-ups or cool-downs for your workouts. However, you can also use these as stand-alone workouts when you just need some fine tuning.

My Big Five (THERE ARE 6) Flow

> 1. Lay on your back and belly or diaphragmatic breathe for one minute.
> 2. Do three rolls left and three rolls right, using upper body.
> 3. Do three rolls left and three rolls right, using lower body.
> 4. Backward barrel roll into the rocking position and rock 20 times with varying foot positions.
> 5. Stay in the rocking position and do 20 head nods up and down. (I also do 10 to the left and right.)
> 6. Finish with 20 standing cross-crawls, knees to elbows.

Post Long Sitting Ops

This RESET flow is one you can do for many situations. If you've been sitting at a computer for too long or conducting convoy operations for example, try this RESET flow when you get the opportunity:

> 1. Stand and breathe for one minute

2. Do 20 standing cross-crawls (forearms to thighs or knees to elbows).
3. Do 20 standing neck nods vertically and 20 horizontally.
4. Do 20 more standing cross-crawls, using either method.

Post Airborne Ops (Parachuting)

1. Lay on back and breathe for one minute.
2. Do three rolls left and three rolls right, using upper body.
3. Do three rolls left and three rolls right, using lower body.
4. Backward barrel roll into the rocking position five times.
5. Stay in the rocking position on the last roll and rock 20 times with varying foot positions.
6. Stay in the rocking position, and do 20 head-nods up and down. Also, do 10 to the left and 10 to the right.
7. Finish with 20 standing cross-crawls (knees to elbows).

Prior to a Physical Fitness Test

- The first step is to do my "Big Five Flow."
- Do 10 pushups and 10 sit-ups.

Specifically for the Army Physical Fitness Test, I do these quick RESET flows between events:

- 10 rocks
- 10 head nods, vertically and horizontally
- 20 standing cross-crawls

Shooting

This RESET flow applies to both training on the range or during a competition. You can do this flow prior to shooting a stage. It will light up your brain and get your reflexes going so you'll be able to shoot to the best of your ability.

1. One minute of breathing
2. 20 standing cross-crawls (forearms to thighs)
3. 10 neck nods vertically and 10 horizontally
4. 10 standing cross-crawls (elbows to knees)

5. 20 rocks (space and ground conditions permitting)

These RESET flows are meant to give you examples of what I use. I recommend starting with these and then being creative on your own once you get a feel for what works for you. A good way to test how your RESET flow is working for you is simply to do an air-squat (butt to ankles) before and after your RESET flow. See if it feels better or not.

You may get some funny looks and questions when you start doing these on the range or during any training, but they work. So let go of your ego, and do them anyway. Get those who stare at you involved as well; eventually, they'll be doing them, too!

11

Working Out with OS

As I spoke about earlier in the book, it's best to look at what your life, job, or hobby requires to determine the right level of physical exertion for your workouts. I'll show you my methodology for deciding what training to do and how OS fits into that.

As always, I recommend warming up and cooling down with at least the Big Five RESETS. Use them periodically during your workout as needed.

Here's the chart I use to help people decide what exercises to start with. I'll go ahead and use an example of how I would fill this out with the goal of being prepared for combat.

Task	Exercise	Notes
Patrol w/Equipment	Ruck 4-6 miles carrying 45 pounds in full equipment. Run 3-6 miles over varying terrain.	The goal is to build strength to carry a load and build endurance for moving long distances under varying conditions and stressors.
Shoot & Move	Burpees, Sprints, Pushups	Burpees for cardio and picking yourself up out of the prone position. Sprints for building leg strength and quickness. Pushups for upper body strength in handling a weapon.
Move a Casualty	Using a dummy or large sandbag (duffel bag) weighing around 175-200 pounds, perform drags for 100 yards and carries for 100 yards.	Use what you have. Include a partner and whatever equipment you may have such as a SKEDCO or drag harness. Take turns.

In the table, you see three examples of tasks and exercises to go along with. For these same tasks, you may have different exercises you'd like to choose. Consider things like the terrain you'll be operating in and the exact equipment you'll have. Obviously, it's not practical to have a M4/AR-15 rifle every time you work out, but use whatever equipment is readily available.

Also, consider your environment. If you're working out in a

populated area, it is probably not a good idea to be kitted up while carrying a rifle. For example, a machine gunner could have a slightly different focus than a normal rifleman. If you're deploying to a location that has relatively flat terrain versus the mountains of Afghanistan, your focus should adapt to that unique environment.

Sticking with the ideas found in *Pressing RESET*, the exercises in my chart can be RESETS. They activate the vestibular system, they cross midline, and/or they engage the gait pattern (opposite limbs moving together). And, if done mindfully, they should incorporate diaphragmatic breathing. I am simply using these exercises to load contralateral movements (the gait pattern) and train the X (the body).

Below is an example of what a firefighter might use to fill out this chart. I consulted with a few firefighters to find out what their most physically demanding tasks are. It's safe to say there are many, but here are a few in the example. Much like a soldier carrying a kit, use your firefighting gear to work out at times. You don't always have to use it, but do it occasionally to get comfortable with how it feels under load and to learn what techniques may work better for doing things like dragging a hose or a body while carrying all your gear.

Task	Exercise	Notes
Fighting Fire	Stair climbs in full turnout gear. Run in running gear.	The goal is to build endurance wearing turnout gear for long periods of time and running is to improve cardio performance.
Forcible Entry	Sledgehammer swings on a tire.	Build explosive power using max effort to pound the tire. Alternate swing techniques and also alternate hitting the side and top of the tire.
Dragging (hose or victims)	Using a dummy or large sandbag (duffel bag) weighing around 175-200 pounds, do drags for 100 yards and carries for 100 yards. Load up a sled with an appropriate weight and use varying dragging/pulling techniques.	Use what you have. Include a partner and whatever equipment you may have such as a SKEDCO or drag harness. Take turns. When dragging the sled, simulate dragging hose.

Using charts like this can help you dial in to what you need to have in your program. These examples can help you get started, but as we say in OS, "you are the chef in your kitchen." Adapt to what you need specifically and what equipment you have available. You may have a full gym available, or you may need to improvise with all of your equipment. All soldiers have duffel bags that can be filled with something for weight, and I'm pretty sure most fire departments have a decommissioned hose that could be used.

Tactical Athlete Workouts

In this section, I'm going to give you some of my workouts. Feel free to use these or modify them and be your own chef. I'll also go over where the RESETS are in each workout (Note: Breathing properly, utilizing your diaphragm as we've discussed, is a RESET in every workout.) These should give you a good idea of how you can apply the principles of pressing RESET in your own workouts and tailor them to what you need.

Something to remember when creating your workouts around *Pressing RESET* is to use the three Original Strength System guidelines:

1. Breathe using your diaphragm.
2. Activate your vestibular system.
3. Engage in contralateral, cross-lateral, or midline crossing movements.

There are three factors I consider when deciding what time to use for exercises:

1. Time allowed for the workout
2. Level of effort (i.e. how hard/fast I want to push on that particular exercise during that particular session)
3. My ability to conduct that exercise to standard for a particular time

Enjoy.

Slam and Carry

You'll need two kettlebells (53 lbs. preferred), a tire, a sledge hammer, and a 50 lbs. sandbag. Place the tire and other equipment at the starting line, and place a marker 30 yards out. The carries will be done down and back for 30 yards. When you perform the sledgehammer swings, make sure you are crossing your midline (your center) with your swings.

> 1. 30 sledgehammer swings (impact top of tire)
> 2. Farmer's carry (kettlebells)
> 3. 30 sledgehammer swings (impact side of tire)
>> 3.1 **Caution:** Practice your technique for hitting the side of the tire as the bounce back can be dangerous. I often impact the tire with the side of the sledge head as that seems to lessen the bounce-back effect.
> 4. Farmer's carry (use sandbag, right-shoulder carry on the way down and left-shoulder carry on the way back)
> 5. 30 sledgehammer swings (impact top of tire)
> 6. Farmer's carry (kettlebells)
> 7. 30 sledgehammer swings (impact side of tire)
> 8. Farmer's carry (front carry sandbag)

Where's the RESET? Here, the RESET can be found in the sledgehammer swings if you work your technique so that you cross the midline of your body. Basically, you should be drawing X's with your sledgehammer from side to side. This is good for your brain, your nervous system, and your body.

Shooter

For this one, you will need a jump box or something to step up on, two weight plates (25 lbs. preferred), a weighted ball or kettlebell (35 lbs. preferred), two cones, and a pair of gloves with a dot on the knuckle of the middle fingers like the ones shown earlier in the book. Place the cones 20 yards apart.

This workout will consist of four rounds of one minute per exercise with one minute of rest between rounds. After the four rounds are complete, finish it off with five minutes of crawling.

> 1. Sprints: Cone to cone. When you get to a cone, you should be facing a "target" to focus on quickly before sprinting back.

2. Step ups: Pinch grip the weight plates, and step up and over the box and then back.
3. Kettlebell draws: See pictures below.
4. Burpees
5. Spiderman crawls: Forward and backward, cone to cone. Focus on the dots on the gloves for four "steps." Then, crawl with head up for four steps.

Where's the RESET? The sprints and crawls are the RESETS in this workout. Both engage the gait pattern with contralateral limb movement. Also, the act of looking at the dots on the gloves and raising the head up activates the vestibular system through practicing head control.

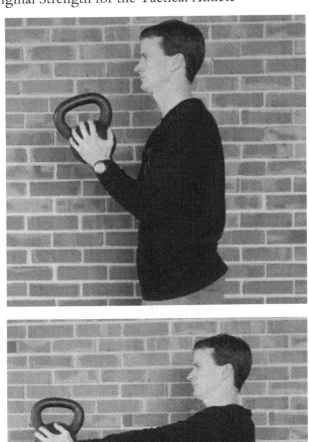

Tight Spaces

I call this one "tight spaces" because I think of crawling in tight spaces with your kit. You can wear your full kit—which I would recommend at least trying at some point—or just use a weighted vest. You will need some weight to drag. I prefer using a sandbag of at least 50 pounds. The only other thing you will need is some flat ground and a hill. Scale the workout based on how much kit you're wearing and the slope and length of your hill.

- Two minutes: Spiderman crawl forward, pulling the sandbag as you crawl (see picture below)
- Three trips: Backward spiderman crawl uphill
- Two minutes: Spiderman crawl laterally (one minute in one direction and one minute in the other direction)
- Repeat five rounds: Determine the amount of rest you need between rounds

Where's the RESET? In this workout, the RESET is obvious; it's the crawling. This is a workout that will be great for tying you together and making you reflexively strong.

Move and Shoot

This one is about moving and shooting. You're going to need four cones and preferably four short-jump boxes that are no higher than two to two-and-a-half feet. You'll also need your firearm of choice and a weighted vest. Finally, you'll need to have a target of your choice positioned at 20 feet from the front of your box setup.

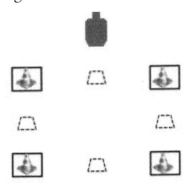

Setup your four cones so that they are around 30 feet apart and form a box. For the first four runs, start wherever you like, but move clockwise, sprinting from cone to cone. At each cone, stop and draw (handgun) or raise (rifle, shotgun) your firearm and dry fire, re-holster, go back to low ready, and sprint to the next cone. Once you have made the run clockwise, reverse and go counter-clockwise. You should do this for a total of four rounds, one round in each direction.

Want to up your game? Take a rest after the first four rounds, and position the jump boxes between the cones. Run this the same way, using the jump boxes as obstacles.

Ensure you're working on your footwork as you start, stop, and sprint from position to position. You should also pay attention to your breathing as that will be important for well-placed shots when it comes time to live fire. Keep your eyes locked on the target/threat. If you're a competition shooter, instead of cones, make some 2'x4' boxes like the ones used in competition so that you can practice your footwork in and out of them. You can use one target, or you can use multiple targets.

Have some fun with this one, and be creative. Play with your box arrangement and target arrangements. Challenge yourself by keeping up with your time and pushing it, but don't sacrifice technique when it comes to utilizing your firearm.

Where's the RESET? Unless you're using a rifle or shotgun, you'll be moving contra laterally as you sprint. When sprinting, the shoulders should be swinging to match the movement of the hips. Also, if you breathe properly, with your diaphragm, you will be better able to control your breathing and heart rate as you take your shots. As you become a practitioner of OS, you will notice how tying yourself together and becoming reflexively stronger will improve your performance in challenging skill workouts like this one.

Over the Wall

This workout requires a wall to pull yourself up and over. If you do not have a wall, I suggest substituting with sets of dips. You'll also need a sandbag of at least 50 pounds and an Olympic bar loaded with two 25-pound plates or as much weight as you're comfortable doing push-presses and front squats with.

Position the bar and sandbag next to the wall.

- 20 front squats
- Five trips over the wall (Throwing the sandbag over the wall and then climbing over equals one trip; Use 10 dips and throw the bag over a pullup bar if you don't have a wall.)
- 20 push-presses
- Repeat five rounds

Where's the RESET? This particular workout doesn't include RESETS, but you will need them before and after, as well as over the next couple of days. Trust me.

Chain Gang

I use the Infinity Strap for this workout plus my 60 pounds of chain. My chain consists of 3-10 foot sections that I link together with carabiners. You'll need 100 yards of good crawling ground to operate on.

- Spiderman crawl 100 yards with chain.
- Run back 100 yards with chain.
- Hold the chain overhead and walk 100 yards down and back. (Use your harness to hold overhead or hold by the chain. The object is to have weight dragging the ground, providing resistance as well. See picture below.)

- Repeat 10 rounds.

Where's the RESET? The RESETS here are in the loaded crawling and running.

Get Up

This workout is all about getting back up with gear on and staying in the fight. You can think of it as being knocked down and having to get back on your feet without the use of your hands as you keep your rifle toward the threat. Or maybe you're a firefighter and can't let go of the hose. In this workout, there will be some quick movement and some slower "grinding" as well.

- 5x Turkish get ups (TGUs): Each arm with at least 1/3 bodyweight. You can use either a kettlebell or sandbag; both provide different dynamics. See pictures below.
- 20 sit up/stand ups (fast paced) with same weight
- 300–yard front-carry farmer's walk: Use what you have, but I prefer two 24 kg. kettlebells in the clean position for this. You can use the same weight for the entire workout, but two weights in each hand are better.
- Repeat for three or five rounds.

Where's the RESET? The TGU is a contra-laterally loaded exercise; thus, it is an amazing exercise for solidifying your center. This is a great workout for focusing on your breathing, keeping your mouth closed as well.

You can see here that I've used the K.I.S.S. (Keep It Stupid Simple) principle with these workouts. I believe in keeping your workouts simple because, the more complicated you make them, the less likely you are to keep your workouts going. Less planning, more work. Many people think they need to create some complex algorithm to get a good workout. I sometimes feel like that's what keeps people from working out and being consistent. For the most part, I only include workouts involving equipment that can be found or made easily. Use what you have. Be creative.

12

Some Words on Training

I've spent quite a bit of time exercising and going through peaks and valleys with my training, so I'd just like to share some things I've learned. Some of these are philosophies I have developed, and they work for me, but they may not for you. Again, take it as you will.

I believe you need to set goals, but with whatever your larger goal is, you need to have smaller goals. For example, if you want to be able to do a one-arm handstand push-up, have some intermediate goals like being able to do a two-arm handstand push-up. This will make your goal more achievable in smaller bites.

As someone who's been in the military for a long time and often believed that you need to be dying in a sweat puddle at the end of every training session, I had to get smarter than that. (I would suggest picking up some books by Pavel Tsatsouline; those books helped me to learn how to strength train.) Working out like that constantly can have adverse effects on your body, so you need to dial it back at times. Am I saying you should cut out those workouts altogether? No. Some people would tell you to, but in a profession with demands such as the infantry, you need to test yourself once in a while and build stamina. The mental toughness it takes cannot be understated.

Ensure you know yourself not just physically but mentally as well. Know your limits, and be creative with building your own mental toughness. When I would run on my own, I always made sure that I stopped my run at or after the point from which I started. So if I started running at my truck when I got out, I made sure I didn't stop until I passed my truck on the way back. This helped me to build a mindset of not stopping until the task has been 100-percent completed.

I believe in listening to the body. Yes, you need to test yourself

89

and workout even when you don't feel like it sometimes, but you should also listen. If your body is telling you that you need a rest, take a rest. It's okay, sometimes. The brain is a wonderful thing and is trying to tell you something. Just like when the sodium in your body is depleted you crave foods rich in salt, your brain sends signals craving some rest. Being sore all the time is not a good thing either.

Don't work so hard that you burn yourself out mentally. Everything will become harder, which may hinder your ability to reach your goals. I believe the same thing concerning dieting. If you're trying to diet to the point that it hinders your social life or becomes an overwhelming task, ease back. You only have one life to live, and you should enjoy it. Now, if you have a health-related issue, do whatever it takes to correct or mitigate it. Too much stress is not good for you, and I've seen too many people add stress to their lives just to get a six pack. If you desperately desire some of these goals, be prepared for the process. Do what makes you happy. Again, you only have one life. Learn to enjoy it.

13

The Adaptability of Original Strength

Adaptability: The ability to maintain composure while responding to or adjusting one's own thinking and actions to fit a changing environment; the ability to think and solve problems in unconventional ways; the ability to proactively shape the environment or circumstances in anticipation of desired outcomes. —ARSOF Core Attributes

Now that you've learned about Original Strength and how it can fit you as a "tactical athlete" in whatever profession you're in, it's time to go forth and get strong. Once you've learned how to execute all the movements and exercises in the Original Strength System, set your goals and achieve them.

Once you have the basics down, **explore your own creativity within OS**. There are many ways you can take the movements within OS and get stronger by exploring ways to make them more dynamic or, in some cases, harder. Be safe in how you do things. Don't get crazy and create injuries; there are plenty of other systems out there doing that.

Another way to be creative is to adapt the movements and explore some regressions if you have an injury. There are ways to "soften" or make some of these movements easier to benefit you if you're injured. Some of these regressions can be found in the Original Strength title book, *Pressing RESET: Original Strength Reloaded*. You can also learn more by attending a *Pressing RESET* workshop. Not only will you learn more at the workshops, you'll also be opened up to a community of people who have been to the OS workshops to whom you can refer for advice at any time.

I've always enjoyed exercises or fitness tools that are "one size fits all" and portable. Other than bodyweight, kettlebells and ropes were my main implements of fitness for a long time. With both of those, you can do so many things in so many places. Tim taught me kettlebells, and John Brookfield taught me his Battling Ropes system. Original Strength is the same way. Don't have room to crawl? Axis crawl. Traveling? Tim travels a lot and does a lot of crawling in hotel hallways. Deployed? No excuses. The Infinity Strap will fit into any duffle bag ever made, and I guarantee you can find something to drag wherever you are.

Original Strength really does take away the excuses for staying strong and resilient. You can sit and do cross-crawls as you take a break from your emails or do as much as a full-on "five-minute flow" before hitting the shoot-house for a day of training. So start practicing your RESETS and seeing how much better you feel. See how they "turn you on" mentally. It's so simple that it just might work.

Don't forget your skill work. While I do believe the Original Strength System is enough for most people, the tactical athlete may need more skill work. What I mean by "skill work" are exercises related specifically to the tasks you conduct. If you're a firefighter who has to sling and drag a lot of hose, try adding in some deadlifting and heavy-rope work. If you're a prison guard and need quick, strong bursts, you probably need to use some heavy weights or kettlebells. (I would recommend kettlebells.) Law enforcement personnel may need to add in some sprints (which is a contralateral RESET) along with some heavy weight work in order to be able to chase down bad guys and take them down. Military personnel will have similar needs in that they may need to move long distances on their feet and be fit to fight when they get there.

So either work OS into your current program, or use what you've learned here to develop a new program. From this point, practice the RESETS and get after it. Our wish is for you to keep your movement, stay resilient, and be reflexively strong until the time you pass on. That's what Original Strength is about.

Follow Original Strength on Facebook and Instagram as well as subscribing on YouTube so you can keep up with the latest and greatest information. I also highly suggest you find a workshop near you and deepen your knowledge of Original Strength. You can also check out the Original Strength website to find an OSSA certified professional to help get you started.

Last but not least, thank you for what you do. If you're out there serving your country—whether it be in the military, law enforcement, firefighting, or whatever your service may be—we want to say THANK YOU. Selfless service is something great and demonstrates the character within you. Be the example for others, and be the change you wish to see in the world.

Now, get out there and go do work!

Learn More About Original Strength

Our mission is to set the world free through movement. As the foundation for all movement for any activity, we teach health and fitness professionals a system that allows for improved patient and client results. We invite you to visit our website at OriginalStrength.net for more information. While on the site, please look at our workshops, videos (Movement SnaxTM), DVDs, equipment and other books. We want to help you move the way you were designed to.

To locate a coach in your area go to https://originalstrength.net/find-a-certified-coach/. We have OS Certified Coaches located around the world.

www.originalstrength.net

"I am fearfully and wonderfully made…" – Psalm 139:14

Printed in Great Britain
by Amazon